Fergus
the Forgetful

The human brain is 80% water.

It's impossible to sneeze and keep your eyes open at the same time.

Vestiphobia is a fear of clothing.

Margaret Ryan and Wendy Smith

Young Lions

JUMBO JETS
Bernie Works a Miracle by Leon Rosselson
Fergus the Forgetful by Margaret Ryan
Forecast of Fear by Keith Brumpton
Sir Quinton Quest Hunts the Yeti
by Kaye Umansky

First published in Great Britain by
A & C Black (Publishers) Ltd 1992
First published in Young Lions 1993
9 8 7 6 5 4 3 2

Young Lions is an imprint of the Children's Division,
part of HarperCollins Publishers Ltd,
77–85 Fulham Palace Road, Hammersmith, London W6 8JB

ISBN 000-674560-1

Printed and bound in Great Britain by
HarperCollins Manufacturing, Glasgow

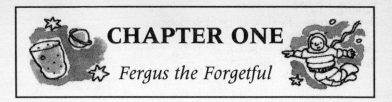

CHAPTER ONE

Fergus the Forgetful

Fergus Ferguson, aged nine years ten months two weeks three and a bit days, forgot things. Not important things like why corks float or how asteroids are made, but unimportant things like wearing matching socks and peeling a banana before eating it.

His forgetfulness got him into trouble.

With his mum . . .

With his dad . . .

With his sister . . .

With his pal . . .

With his teacher . . .

'Well, it won't do,' went on Miss Jenner.
'You sit there and write me out five
reasons why you forgot your P.E. kit. If
they're good reasons I won't write a note
to your parents. If not . . .'

So Fergus wrote out five reasons.

The first one was easy. The second one was quite easy. The third one was harder. The fourth one was a real slog.

① I forgot my P.E. Kit because I am forgetful.

② I forgot my P.E. Kit because I am very forgetful.

③ I forgot my P.E. Kit because I am very very forgetful.

④ I forgot my P.E. Kit because I am very very very forgetful.

But number five came to him in a flash.

⑤ I forgot my P.E kit because my mind was on more important things.

Surely Miss Jenner would be impressed with that.

She wasn't. The note went home to his parents.

So now Fergus was in trouble with his teacher, his mum, his dad and his big sister Tracey who couldn't believe she was related to someone as thick, dim and cotton-woolly-headed as Fergus. And she told him so. At great length.

CHAPTER TWO

Big news at school

After the note from Miss Jenner, a row from his mum and dad and ear nipping verbals from Tracey, Fergus promised he would try to improve.

He got up early next morning and dressed very carefully. He checked that he was wearing two socks the same, two shoes the same, two ties . . . oops. Then he put on his sweater and went downstairs to have breakfast.

His mum looked at him, said nothing, but carefully lifted one of his ears and peered behind it.

'Have you washed this morning, Fergus?'

And Fergus, don't forget to put your trousers on this time. It'll be a bit chilly going to school in your underpants.

'Oh no!' said Fergus, and dashed back upstairs.

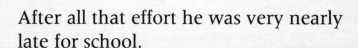

After all that effort he was very nearly late for school.

'Where have you been?' said Robbie, waiting for him at the school gate. 'Come on, there's a special notice up on the noticeboard. You've just got time to have a quick look before old Jenner comes in.'

Fergus had a quick look. Robbie was right. The notice was special.

WIN A COMPUTER FOR YOUR SCHOOL

INTER-SCHOOL QUIZ
EGLINGTON STREET SCHOOL
v
ST BARTHOLOMEW'S SCHOOL

WILL ALL PRIMARY SIX PUPILS WISHING TO TAKE PART IN THIS QUIZ PLEASE WRITE THEIR NAMES BELOW
E.Boyd
Headmaster

Footba
x1

KATS
for free

Fergus and Robbie looked at the list of pupils who had already volunteered:

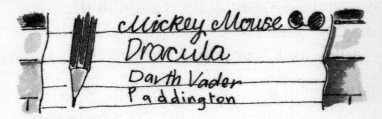

Mickey Mouse
Dracula
Darth Vader
Paddington

'I get the feeling no one's taking this seriously,' said Fergus.

'Can't blame them,' said Robbie. 'St Barty's will knock spots off us. They're all miles brainier than we are. And they cheat. They only beat us in the football tournament last year because of a foul.'

Fergus nodded sympathetically. He'd seen the foul, and Robbie, who had been playing had been on the receiving end of it. Then the bell rang and they had to go into their classroom.

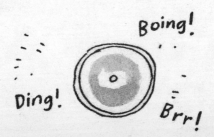

Boing!

Ding!

Brr!

Miss Jenner was in a foul mood. She had the results of yesterday's spelling test in her hand, and they were not good.

Matilda, the plural of mouse is not mouses.

Elizabeth, the plural of house is not hice.

Robbie, worm does not have a u in it.

Fergus, there is no K in cannot.

'But there's a K in knot,' thought Fergus. 'So why not a K in canknot? Or even two Ks, kanknot. That would be a much more interesting word.' The trouble with Miss Jenner was she had no sense of adventure when it came to spelling.

KANKNOT TONKNAK KXZW

Just then there was a knock at the door
and Mr Boyd, the headmaster, entered.
He had the list of volunteers for the
Inter-School Quiz in his hand.

'Some people . . . ,' he said, looking at
class six through narrowed eyes, 'are not
taking this Inter-School Quiz seriously
enough. This competition has been
sponsored by Mr Greaves, editor of our
local newspaper, and is a great opportunity
for you to win a valuable prize for
Eglington Street School. The school will
be very proud of you when you win.'

'Fat chance of that,' muttered Robbie.

'Now, if you think your general knowledge is up to it, I suggest you put your *proper* name down on this sheet of paper. Miss Jenner will test your general knowledge and choose the four best people from this class.'

Then the headmaster left, and the whole class signed the paper with their proper names.

Fergus Yorick Ferguson
Robert Munroe
Yolanda Mary-Louisa Day
June Ecclesworthy
DARREN SHIPLEY
Jamel Akib
Bidisha Parikh
Elizabeth Marigold May
Gary Burton
Leonora Komonski

Miss Jenner sighed when she looked at it. She'd intended going over the spelling, but a general knowledge test it had to be.

She wrote ten questions up on the blackboard. Fergus rubbed his hands when he saw them. Now was his chance to prove that he wasn't all those names Tracey had called him . . .

When the answers had been checked, Fergus came out on top with nine out of ten. He got number four wrong.

Robbie, Bidisha and Elizabeth were next best with seven out of ten. Miss Jenner shook her head.

'It looks like Fergus has to be captain of the quiz team, with Robbie, Bidisha and Elizabeth as the other members. Well done all of you, though I can't say I'm happy about you representing the school, Fergus, not with your memory. So I'm giving you fair warning, between now and the quiz next Tuesday if you forget your P.E. kit or leave your homework jotter on the kitchen table, or have any other lapses of memory, you're out of the quiz. I'll choose another person from the list instead. Do you understand?'

Fergus nodded and crossed his fingers, his toes and his eyes.
'No problem, Miss Jenner,' he said. 'I'll remember everything.' Then he leaned over to Robbie and whispered:

CHAPTER THREE

Ways of remembering

Fergus dragged his school-bag along the
ground all the way home from school
that day. He always did that when he was
worried about something.

But Fergus was still worried. He made a little trail of salt along the table-cloth at tea-time that night while he told his family about the quiz.

Robbie might not remind me of everything. I might still forget things.

Don't worry. We'll all help. The first thing you should do is make a list of all the things you must remember.

Fergus stopped worrying about the list and the hanky, and started worrying about Tracey.

But later on that night she came into his bedroom while he was reading the children's encyclopaedia.

'I bought you these,' she said, 'to help you concentrate.'

And she handed him a large packet of his favourite chewy chocolate caramels.

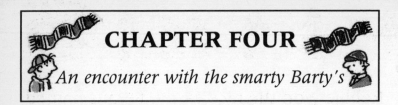

CHAPTER FOUR

An encounter with the smarty Barty's

True to his word Robbie appeared early
next morning to check that Fergus hadn't
forgotten anything.

Robbie waited patiently until Fergus had
finished his homework.

'Race you to the shop, I want to get some
crisps for break-time.'

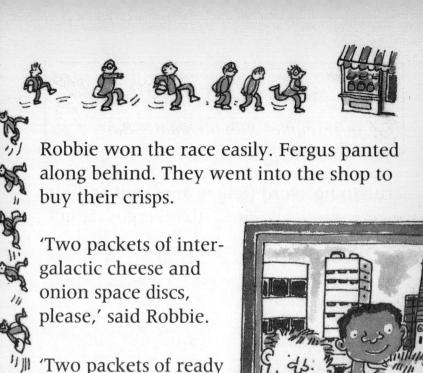

Robbie won the race easily. Fergus panted along behind. They went into the shop to buy their crisps.

'Two packets of inter-galactic cheese and onion space discs, please,' said Robbie.

'Two packets of ready salted, please,' said Fergus.

Suddenly, the shop door flew open and a crowd of boys from St Bartholomew's school charged in.

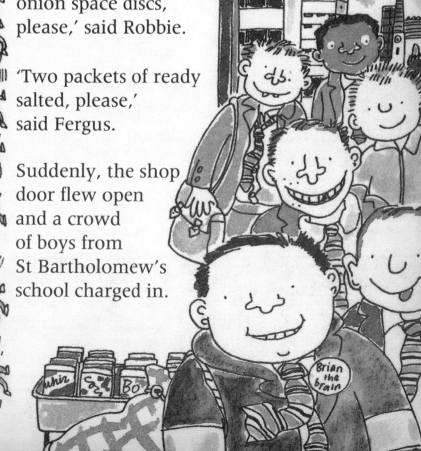

'Well well,' said a large boy with *Brian the brain* written on his lapel badge. 'Look who's here. A couple of little soft boiled eggies from Eglington Street. Move aside, little eggies, and make room for the smarties from St Barty's.'

'Smarties, huh,' said Robbie, who had more courage than sense. 'We'll soon see who the smarties are when we beat you in the quiz.'

'Ah ha, so you're in the quiz, are you? You and who else?'

'Bidisha Parikh, Elizabeth May and Fergus. He's the team captain and a real brainbox.'

Brian the brain gave a disbelieving snort.

'You, Fergus Ferguson. Fergus the
forgetful. Then there's no contest. You
can hardly even remember your own
name. You might as well give up now.
We'll hammer you into the ground. We'll
nail you to the wall. We'll eradicate you
completely.'

'No way,' said Fergus.

'No chance,' said Robbie.

'And that's just what you've got of
winning the quiz against my team,'
sneered Brian. 'I'm what you're up
against; me, Brian the brain.'

Fergus and Robbie slid out of the shop.
'We're really in trouble now, Robbie,' said
Fergus as they headed for school. 'Didn't
Brian win that crossword competition in
the local paper?'

'That was a fix. His uncle's the editor. Maybe this competition's a fix too, but don't worry, Fergus, we've got you as our captain. We'll be all right.'

But Fergus did worry. He started dragging his school-bag again. Then he stopped, opened up both bags of crisps and ate them all.

'I thought your crisps were for break-time,' said Robbie.

'They were,' said Fergus. 'But I'm starving and I've just remembered why. I forgot to eat my breakfast.'

The day in school passed quietly enough. Fergus listened so carefully to what Miss Jenner told him to do that his ears ached. But Miss Jenner seemed pleased with the effort and gave the quiz team time off in the afternoon to go to the school library and do a bit of swotting.

They were just having
a good giggle when
the headmaster,
Mr Boyd, walked in.

'I wanted to tell you
how much Eglington
Street School is relying
on you in this quiz,'
he said. 'Are we going
to win?'

'Ah . . . Um . . . Er,' the team muttered,
and scuffed their feet under the table.

'I'm pretty good at general knowledge
myself,' Mr Boyd went on. 'So I want you
to ask me anything you like, and I'll
answer it. Okay? Go on, ask me
something.'

The quiz team glanced at each other then
studied their fingernails.

Interesting things fingernails, sometimes.

'Go on. I'm ready. Ask me something.'

'Ask him something, Fergus,' hissed the rest of the team. 'Or we'll never get on with learning anything.'

Fergus's mind was a total blank. Then he looked at Mr Boyd's bald head, and said the first thing he thought of.

Mr Boyd's bushy eyebrows shot up. 'Are you being impertinent, Fergus?'

'NNNNNNo, sir. It's just that I was reading about it in this book. Hair grows about half an inch a month and quickest between ten and eleven in the morning.'

'Really?' said Mr Boyd. 'How fascinating. Well, I'll leave you now to carry on working, but I'll borrow that book if I may, Fergus.'

'Yes sir,' said Fergus, handing it over. 'You'll find the bit about hair under the letter H.'

CHAPTER FIVE

Trouble

Fergus swung his school-bag round his head as he walked home that afternoon. The good day at school had made him feel a lot more cheerful. He had just clunked himself on the head with his bag when two large shadows fell across his path.

Fergus looked up. It was Brian the brain and his pal Muscles. Fergus's cheerful mood vanished.

'What do you want?' asked Fergus, wishing Robbie were still around.

'This will do for a start,' said Brian, and snatched Fergus's school-bag.

'Here, give that back.'

'Come and get it,' called Brian as he and Muscles ran off.

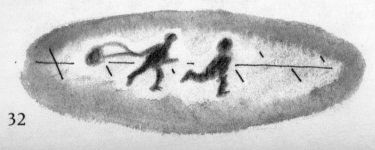

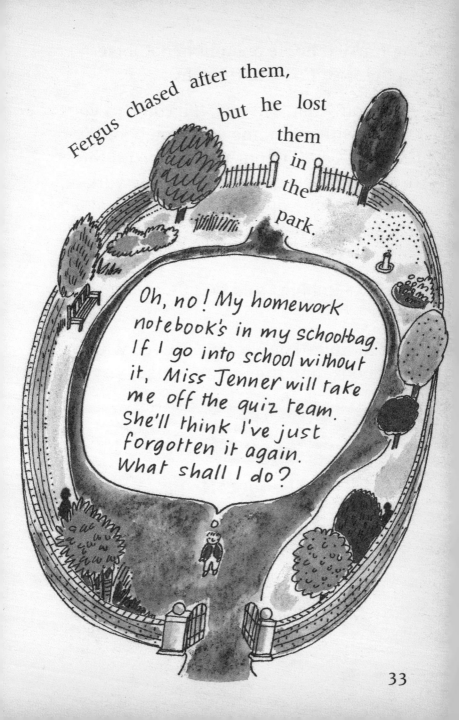

Fergus chased after them, but he lost them in the park.

Oh, no! My homework notebook's in my schoolbag. If I go into school without it, Miss Jenner will take me off the quiz team. She'll think I've just forgotten it again. What shall I do?

33

He hurried home and phoned Robbie. Robbie listened and thought . . .

'Tell you what,' he said. 'I'll come to your house with my homework notebook. We'll re-cover it, put your name on the front, and you can do your homework in it. I'll do mine on a piece of paper and tell Miss Jenner it's my school-bag that's lost. She won't take me off the team.'

'Thanks Robbie,' said Fergus. 'You're a pal.'

Ten minutes later Robbie arrived with the notebook, and they set to work.

Then Tracey appeared. 'You two are up to something,' she said.

Fergus told her what had happened.

Fergus and Robbie waited while Tracey went out into the hall to telephone.

Five minutes later she was back.

'Your school-bag is in the green litter bin at the park gate,' she said. 'Go and get it now.'

'Thanks Tracey,' said Fergus. 'But how did you find out?'

'That creep, Raymond, has been trying to make a date with me for ages so I promised I'd go out with him on Saturday afternoon if he found out what Brian had done with your school-bag.'

'Thanks Tracey. You're a pal.'

'No,' said Tracey. 'I'm a sister. Go and get your school-bag.'

Fergus went. Sure enough the bag was in the litter bin at the park gate. But as he pulled it out, he suddenly realised that being forced to tell where it was would not have pleased Brian the brain one little bit. He would be nastier than ever.

'Now I'll really have to watch out,' thought Fergus, and ran home at a speed that was almost fast.

CHAPTER SIX

In the library

The next morning was a Saturday and the team had agreed to meet outside the local library at ten o'clock to have a look at the encyclopaedias. Everyone was there on time except Fergus.

Still no Fergus – not a toe, not a pinkie, not a hair of Fergus's head had appeared.

Then a sorry sight came panting round the corner; trainers unlaced, jacket undone, hair uncombed. Fergus.

The library was busy with toddlers looking at the picture books, parents looking after the toddlers, and librarians looking all round to make sure there was no nonsense.

Fergus and his team collected all the encyclopaedias and took them to a big table by the window.

'We'll never learn all this in one morning,' wailed Bidisha.

'No need to learn it all,' said Fergus. 'Robbie, you take *Inventions and Discoveries*. Bidisha, you take *The Human Body*, and Elizabeth, you take *Our World*. I'll take *Miscellaneous*.'

'Miss who?' said Robbie.

'Fascinating,' said Bidisha. 'Do you know that when our eyelids move up and down they act like built-in windscreen wipers?'

'Make a note in case you forget,' said Fergus.

Bidisha stuck out her tongue at him.

'Great,' said Fergus. 'At this rate we'll easily beat St Barty's.'

He had just opened up his own volume of the encyclopaedia when, through the big library window, he spied a familiar figure – Brian the brain.

'Quick! Under the table everybody,' hissed Fergus, and dived for the floor.

'Well,' said Brian the brain, swaggering into the library. 'If it isn't the little eggie team, trying to put knowledge into their little eggie heads. All keen and eager to swot up for the quiz are you? Well you can swot till the cows come home. Take it from one who knows, you haven't a chance of winning.'

'Oh yes we have,' said Robbie. 'We're learning some very interesting things.'

43

The toddlers dropped their picture books and came to see what was going on.

The parents dropped their conversations and came to see what was going on.

44

The librarians dropped everything and threw Brian and his gang and Fergus and his team out of the library.

'What are we going to do now that we're banned from the library?' worried Fergus, rubbing his chin and dragging his jacket along the ground. 'Who'd have thought that a little learning could be such a dangerous thing?'

CHAPTER SEVEN

The video

Fergus's mum and dad were not pleased about the library ban.

'I'll never be able to look the librarians in the face again,' said his mum.

'Only hooligans get banned from the library,' said his dad. 'It's never happened to anyone in this family before.'

'Yes it has,' said Tracey. 'I was banned for a week once for dropping a stink bomb in the romance section.'

'Tracey, how could you?' said her parents.

'It was a dare,' said Tracey. 'And a lot less daring than having a date with creepy Raymond.

Bing Bong = Bing Bong

'That'll be him now. I'm telling you, if he even tries to hold my hand, I shall throw up all over him.'

46

Tracey left for her date.

Mr Ferguson left to watch his football match, and Mrs Ferguson put a chicken in the oven for tea and left Fergus to watch it while she went shopping. Fergus settled down to some worrying. He got out his old teddy bear and dragged it up and down the sitting-room carpet.

He always dragged his old teddy when there was some really serious worrying to do. He worried and dragged and dragged and worried so much that he completely forgot to take the chicken out of the oven in time . . .

'I'll go and get a take-away,' sighed his dad when he came back from the football.

'Yuk. That smell reminds me of creepy Raymond's aftershave,' said Tracey when she came back from her date. 'Speaking of Raymond, I've got something for you, Fergus.' And she handed Fergus a video.

'Thanks Trace, but I'm too busy worrying right now to watch a video,' said Fergus.

'Look at the title.'

'Tracey, you're brilliant,' he screeched, nearly forgetting himself and kissing her. 'That can teach us a lot. Imagine thinking of that.'

'I didn't actually,' said Tracey. 'Raymond told me that's what his brother's team are learning for the quiz, so I borrowed the same video for you. Now, phone your pals and get them over here after tea to watch it. That way at least you'll know all the answers the other team knows.'

'Right,' said Fergus. 'I'll phone right away.'

'Good idea,' said Tracey. 'Before you forget.'

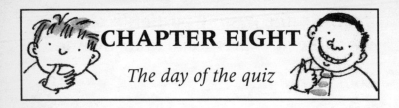

CHAPTER EIGHT

The day of the quiz

On the day of the quiz, Robbie walked Fergus right back to his front gate after school. 'Everything's going to be fine now, Fergus. You can stop dragging your school-bag along the road. You can stop worrying. I'll see you at the town hall at seven o'clock. Don't be late.'

Fergus wasn't late. He was so anxious that he went on ahead of his family and was early. But Brian the brain and his team were earlier still.

Mrs Blair, the gossipy postmistress who was to ask the questions, came over to them.

The town hall gradually filled. Mrs Blair
called everyone to order and introduced
Mr Greaves, the editor of the Gazette.

Fergus kept a close eye on Mr Greaves and was sure he saw him wink at Brian the brain.

'At least we know the answers to the same questions they do,' muttered Robbie.

But they didn't . . .

CHAPTER NINE

Who will win?

Mrs Blair put on her thick glasses and the competition began.

'Mr Greaves and I have worked out these questions very carefully,' she said. 'I know you young people like to watch quite a lot of television so we'll start with questions from one of my favourite TV quiz shows.'

And so it went on . . .

St Bartholomew's answered question after question correctly. But it was a poor start for Eglington Street who fell further and further behind.

'We've been tricked.' Fergus was grim. 'We've been learning the questions and answers from a different video. Brian must have fed the wrong information to Raymond.'

One look at the smirk on Brian the brain's face told Fergus he was right.

St Bartholomew's raced further and further ahead, and Eglington Street, despite Fergus and his head full of important facts, was struggling.

'And now we come to the quick-fire-question section of the quiz,' announced Mrs Blair. 'Contestants must answer ''yes'' or ''no'', and the team with the most correct answers in five minutes wins ten bonus points.'

The smarty Barty's supporters were jubilant as their team answered question after question correctly. They yelled and cheered and waved their school scarves.

The Eggie Street supporters slid down lower and lower in their chairs. All that is, except Tracey. She had been watching Mr Greaves and had noticed that he always blew his nose if the answer to the smarty Barty's quiz question was 'yes'.

'So that's how they're doing it,' she muttered. She left her seat and pushed her way into one right behind Mr Greaves. Then she took out her can of coke, gave it a really good shake, and pulled the ring.

Mr Greaves was drenched.

'Oh, silly me. I am sorry,' said Tracey as Mr Greaves hurried dripping from the room.

From that moment Fergus and his team started to pull up. But even when they won the bonus points for the quick-fire-questions, St Bartholomew's didn't look worried. Thanks to their runaway start, they still had a very good lead.

Soon the teams were neck and neck.

Mrs Blair looked at her watch then looked at the score.

'Now,' she said, 'since the team points are equal we will play for a decider. These questions will be answered only by the team captains.'

Brian looked confident. He knew he was brainy. Fergus looked worried. He knew he was forgetful. Suppose in the heat of the moment he stopped remembering all the important things like why corks float or what an asteroid is? Suppose he started remembering things like wearing matching socks and peeling a banana before eating it? Suppose he let everybody down, his teacher, his mum and dad, his sister and Eggie Street School?

Then he felt his elbow being nudged.
'You can do it, Fergus,' whispered Robbie.
'You're a real brainbox. Now's your
chance to show everyone you're not
thick, dim, stupid and cotton-woolly-
headed.'

Fergus nodded and concentrated on the
questions. They started off easy but got
steadily harder and harder. Finally Brian
the brain got stuck on one.

Brian screwed up his forehead and racked
his brains. Fergus could almost hear him
thinking. Finally he shook his head.

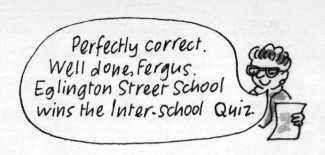

Perfectly correct. Well done, Fergus. Eglington Street School wins the Inter-school Quiz.

Fergus the forgetful could hardly believe it. Brian the brain could hardly believe it. His uncle, Mr Greaves, the damp sticky editor of the Gazette, could hardly believe it. But Eggie Street School *could* believe it. Thanks to Fergus they had at last won something.

There was a tremendous noise of cheering and clapping. Not only that, there was Fergus's mum and dad actually doing a little dance with Mr Boyd and Miss Jenner. And, not to be outdone, Tracey was standing up on her seat yelling FER-GUS, FER-GUS, FER-GUS. As Fergus went to receive his prize from Mr Greaves, he thought, 'Tracey'll probably get banned from the town hall now.'

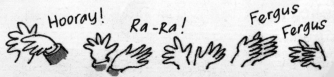

Then Mr Greaves and the not-so-smarty Barty's slunk away as Fergus shook hands with his team. 'You were great everybody,' he said. 'Just great.'

'So were you,' they all said and thumped him on the back.

'And I'll never call you thick, dim, stupid and cotton-woolly-headed ever again,' said Tracey, coming up and giving him a big kiss. 'At least, not for the rest of today.'

~~~us the forgetful
~~~~~ at her and